The Secrets of Space
Edwin George Plalickal
ISBN: 978-1-8382744-1-2

Published By: -

i2i
PUBLISHING

i2i Publishing. Manchester.
www.i2ipublishing.co.uk

Introduction

Space *is amazing. It is completely silent. Our galaxy is the Milky Way. We live on Earth, the only planet ever found with life on it. Scientists are now finding other planets with life on them.*
It has been estimated that our galaxy has approximately 200 billion stars.
Imagination will often carry us to worlds that never were. But without imagination we would go nowhere...

Life. If we didn't have life, we wouldn't be here. We, humans, have lungs to breathe. The mammals, birds and reptiles also have lungs, but fish have gills to breathe. Scientists say that every breath we breathe is from the ocean plants. These ocean plants which help us to breathe are called phytoplankton. We have a nose to breathe in and a mouth to breathe out. Or you can use your nose to breathe out and your mouth to breathe in. These phytoplankton, like other plants, photosynthesise - use sunlight and carbon dioxide to make food.

5

The Planets

Mercury

Mercury is the closest planet to the solar system. It does not have any moons or rings. Your weight on Mercury would be 38% of your weight on Earth. A day on Mercury lasts 88 days. It is the fastest planet that orbits the Sun and it is a little bigger than the Earth's moon. The surface on Mercury is covered by craters caused by the impact of space rocks. You may think that Mercury is the hottest planet in the solar system, but it is not. It is not the hottest planet in the solar system because it does not have much of an atmosphere to trap heat. The hottest planet in the solar system is Venus. Mercury is not easily seen because of its closeness, except during twilight. For every two orbits of the Sun, Mercury completes three rotations about its axis. Up until 1965 it was thought that the same side of Mercury constantly faced the Sun. Thirteen times a century Mercury can be observed from the Earth, passing across the face of the Sun in an event called a transit, the next will occur on November 13th 2032. Mercury is nearly tidally locked to the Sun and over time this has slowed the rotation of the planet to almost match its orbit around the Sun. Mercury also has the highest orbital eccentricity of all the planets with its distance from the Sun ranging from 46 to 70 million km. It is just 4,879 kilometres across its equator, compared with 12,742 kilometres for Earth. Each cubic centimetre of Mercury has a density of 5.4 grams with only Earth having a higher density. It is this dense because of the heavy metals and rocks on the planet. The planet Mercury has wrinkles. Scientists named these wrinkles Lobate Scarps. These can be up to a mile high and hundreds of miles long. Mercury has a molten core. In recent years scientists from NASA believed the solid iron core of smaller planets cool rapidly, but after some in depth research, the results were not in line with those who expected solidity.

Venus

Venus (Roman goddess of love and beauty) is the second planet closest to the Sun and the third brightest object in the night sky after the Sun and the Moon. It is sometimes known as the *sister planet* to Earth because its size and mass are really similar. It has a magnitude of -3.8 to -4.6, which makes it clear on a bright day. Venus is sometimes known as the *morning star* and the *evening star*. In the olden times, ancient civilisations believed that Venus was in fact two distinct stars appearing in the night sky. When the orbit of Venus overtakes the orbit of the Earth, it changes from being visible at sunlight to being visible at sunset.

Earth

Earth is the third planet from the Sun and the only astronomical object known to harbour life. According to radiometric dating and other evidence, Earth formed over 4.5 billion years ago. Earth's gravity interacts with other objects in space, especially the Sun and the Moon, which is Earth's only natural satellite. In addition to being our home and the place where life as we know it originated, it remains the only planet we know of where life thrives. And over the course of the past few centuries, we have learned much about Earth, which has only deepened our fascination with it. Earth is the only planet not named after a god or goddess in Greek mythology. Our planet was once believed to be in the centre of the Universe.

Mars

Mars is the fourth planet from the Sun and last of the terrestrial planets. Like the rest of the planets, except Earth, Mars is named after a Greek mythological figure – the Roman god of war. Mars is also called the *red planet* due to the reddish colour of its surface. It is the second smallest planet in the solar system. Mars is around 227,940,000 km from the Sun. Chinese astronomers called Mars the *Fire Star* while ancient Egyptian priests called it *Her Desher* meaning 'the red one'. The landmass of Mars and Earth is remarkably similar. You could jump on Mars three times higher than you can jump on Earth. Only 16 of the 39 Mars missions were successful. In 2022, Europe's Exobiology on Mars program will continue to search (following the first mission in 2016) the planet for signs of Martian life, study the surface and terrain of the planet and map potential environmental hazards to future manned missions to Mars. Pieces of Mars have been found on Earth. It is believed that trace amounts of the Martian atmosphere were within meteorites that the planet ejected. These meteorites then orbited the solar system for millions of years amongst the other objects and solar debris before eventually entering the Earth's atmosphere and crashing to the ground. The study of this material has allowed scientists to discover more about Mars before launching space missions. Mars was once believed to be home to intelligent life. This came from the discovery of lines or grooves in the surface called *canali* by Italian astronomer Giovanni Schiaparelli. He believed that these were not naturally occurring and were proof of intelligent life. However, these were later shown to be an optical illusion. The tallest mountain known in the solar system is on Mars. This mountain, called Olympus Mons, was formed billions of years ago. It may still be active because people have found evidence of volcano lava. The Sun looks about half the size it does from Earth when seen from Mars. When Mars is closest to the Sun in its orbit the southern hemisphere points toward the Sun and this causes a noticeably short but fiercely hot summer. In the north it experiences a brief but cold winter.

Jupiter

Named after the Roman king of the gods, Jupiter is fitting of its name. With a mass of 1.90 x 1027 kg and a mean diameter of 139,822 km, Jupiter is easily the largest planet in the Solar System. To put this in perspective, it would take 11 Earths lined up next to each other to stretch from one side of Jupiter to the other and it would take 317 Earths to equal the mass of Jupiter. Jupiter has 67 confirmed moons orbiting the planet. These moons are separated into three groups:

Inner moons. These orbit the closest to Jupiter and are sometimes called the Amalthea group. The names of the inner moons of Jupiter are Metis, Adrastea, Amalthea and Thebe.

Galilean moons. These are largest of Jupiter's moons and were discovered by Galileo Galilei in 1610 – Io, Europa, Ganymede and Calisto.

Outer moons. These moons are much smaller and further away from Jupiter. They also have irregular, elliptical orbit paths and many are captured asteroids.

The first recorded sighting of Jupiter was by the ancient Babylonians in around 7th or 8th century BC. It is named for Jupiter, the king of the Roman gods and god of the Sky.

The Greek equivalent is Zeus, god of thunder. For the Mesopotamians, he was the god Marduk and patron of the city of Babylon. Germanic tribes saw the planet as Donor, also known as Thor.

When Galileo discovered the four moons of Jupiter in 1610, this was the first proof of celestial bodies orbiting something other than Earth. The discovery also provided further evidence of Copernicus' Sun-centred solar system model. Jupiter has the shortest day of the eight planets. Jupiter rotates very quickly, turning on its axis once every 9 hours and 55 minutes. This rapid rotation is also what causes the flattening effect of the planet, which is why it has an oblate shape. One orbit of the Sun takes Jupiter 11.86 Earth years. This means that when viewed from Earth, the planet appears to move very slowly in the sky. It takes months for Jupiter to move from one constellation to the next. Jupiter has a faint ring system around it.

Saturn

Saturn is the sixth planet from the Sun and second largest planet of the Solar System in terms of diameter and mass. If compared, it is easy to see why Saturn and Jupiter have been designated as relatives. From atmospheric composition to rotation, these two planets are extremely similar. Due to these factors, Saturn was named after the father of the god Jupiter in Roman mythology. Saturn is the sixth planet from the Sun, and last of the planets known to ancient civilizations. It was known to the Babylonians and Far Eastern observers. Saturn is one of five planets able to be seen with the naked eye. It is also the fifth brightest object in the solar system. In Roman mythology Saturn was the father of Jupiter, king of the gods. This relationship makes sense given that the planets Saturn and Jupiter are similar in so many respects, including size and composition. The Greek counterpart is known as Cronus. The most common nickname for Saturn is *The Ringed Planet,* a nickname arising from the large, beautiful and extensive ring system that encircles the planet. These rings are mostly made from chunks of ice and carbonaceous dust. They stretch out more than 12,700 km from the planet but are only a mere 20 m thick. Saturn gives off more energy than it receives from the Sun. This unusual quality is believed to be generated from the gravitational compression of the planet combined with the friction from the large amount of helium found within its atmosphere.

It takes Saturn 29.4 Earth years to orbit the Sun. This slow movement against a backdrop of stars led to the planet being nicknamed *Lubadsagush* – or 'oldest of the old' – by the ancient Assyrians. Saturn has the fastest winds of any other planet in our solar system. These winds have been measured at approximately 1,800 km per hour (1,100 mi. per hour). Saturn is the least dense planet in the solar system. It is made mostly of hydrogen and has a density which is less than water – which technically means that Saturn would float. The layers of hydrogen get denser further into the planet, eventually becoming metallic and leading to a hot interior core. Saturn has 150 moons and smaller moonlets. All of these moons are frozen – the largest of which are Titan and Rhea. The moon Enceladus also appears to have an ocean hidden below its frozen surface. Saturn's moon Titan is the second largest moon in the Solar System, behind Jupiter's moon Ganymede.

Uranus

Uranus is the seventh planet from the Sun in the solar system. It is a gas giant and the third largest planet in the solar system. It is made of ice, gases and liquid metal. The atmosphere contains hydrogen, helium and methane. It is not visible to the naked eye and became the first planet discovered by a telescope. It is tipped on its side by 98 degrees. It is often described as 'rolling around the Sun on its side.' When you could see it through your naked eye, it was not recognised as a planet due to its dimness and slow orbit. According to Greek mythology, it is also named after the Greek god of the sky. It was the husband of Gaia, the goddess of Earth. It was discovered by William Herschel on December 13, 1781. William Herschel was a German-born British astronomer. The orbital speed of Uranus is 14,763 mi./hr (6.6 km/sec).

Neptune

Neptune is the eighth planet from the Sun and last of the known planets. While it is the third largest planet with respect to mass, it is only the fourth largest in terms of diameter. Due to its blue colouration, Neptune was named after the Roman god of the Sea. It takes Neptune 164.8 Earth years to orbit the Sun. On July 11 2011, Neptune completed its first full orbit since its discovery in 1846. Neptune was discovered by Jean Joseph Le Verrier. The planet was not known to ancient civilizations because it is not visible to the naked eye. The planet was initially called *Le Verrier* after its discoverer. This name, however, quickly was abandoned and the name Neptune was chosen instead. In Greek mythology, Neptune is called Poseidon. Neptune has the second largest gravity of any planet in the solar system - second only to Jupiter. The orbit path of Neptune is approximately 30 astronomical units (AU) from the Sun. This means it is around 30 times the distance from the Earth to the Sun. The largest Neptunian moon, Triton, was discovered just 17 days after Neptune itself was discovered. Neptune has a storm similar the Great Red Spot on Jupiter. It is commonly known as the Great Dark Spot and is roughly the size of

Earth. Neptune also has a second storm called the Small Dark Spot. This storm is around the same size as Earth's moon.

Nebulas

Nebulas are a mixture of the gasses hydrogen and helium, as well as dust and plasma. The beautiful pictures the Hubble Space Telescope beams down are actually three different channels of black and white, which are mixed and painted by scientists to produce the vibrant colours we see in magazines and television. The layers are painted according to the composition of the different gasses within the specific nebula. The word nebula means 'cloud' in Latin. The galaxy Andromeda was initially believed to be a nebula before Edwin Hubble proved that Andromeda was actually a galaxy of its own in the 1920's. Before then, it was believed that other galaxies were merely nebulas and that the universe only consisted of the Milky Way. Nebulas are often the result of a giant star or a white dwarf exploding which is called a supernova.

The crab nebula was formed by a supernova in the year 1054. This event was observed by many cultures during this time. Stars can be born inside nebulas, such as the crab pulsar which resides within the Crab Nebula. The crab pulsar is an extremely young, spinning star, which emits radio waves. The Cat's Eye Nebula, recognisable in pictures because of

its vivid colours and vague resemblance to an eye is a planetary nebula.
Planetary nebulae are emission nebulae and often form in the wake of white dwarfs. These are their names or references: Barnard's Loop, Boomerang Nebula, Bubble Nebula, NGC 7635, Bubble Nebula in Barnard's Galaxy, Cave Nebula, NGC 281, Pacman Nebula, NGC 306, NGC 346, NGC 371, NGC 395, NGC 588, NGC 595, NGC 604, NGC 1435, Reflection nebula in the Pleiades, NGC 1491, NGC 1579, NGC 1714, NGC 1715, NGC 1788, NGC 1931, NGC 1973, NGC 1975 and NGC 1977, NGC 1999, NGC 2014, NGC 2023, NGC 2080, Ghost Head Nebula, NGC 2174, NGC 2261, NGC 2736, the Pencil Nebula, NGC 3576, NGC 3603, NGC 6188, NGC 6193, NGC 6334, NGC 6357, NGC 6559, NGC 6589, NGC 6590, NGC 6914, NGC 7129, LHA 120-N55, vdB1, IC 349, IC 2177, IC 2631, IC 5146.
The layers are painted according to the composition of the different gasses within the specific nebula. The crab nebula was formed by a supernova in the year 1054.

Galaxies

There are lots of galaxies in the universe. Scientists have been finding how many galaxies there are in the universe and have estimated that there are 200 billion galaxies in the universe. In the best sky conditions, the naked eye (with effort) can see objects with an apparent magnitude of 8.0. This reveals about 43,197 objects in the sky.
There are 9 galaxies visible to the naked eye that you might see when observing the sky, and there are about 13 nebulae that you might see. Our galaxy is called the Milky Way and was found by Galileo Galei.
Galileo Galilei was born on February 15th, 1564.
Our neighbour galaxy is called Andromeda and Andromeda was discovered by Edwin Hubble. Edwin Hubble has also invented a telescope of great length and you can see really far through it. Our galaxy, The Milky Way, contains lots and lots of stars and it also contains 8 planets which are: Mercury, Venus, Earth, Mars, Jupiter, Saturn, Uranus and Neptune.
William Herschel found and named the galaxy called Antennae. The Antennae galaxy also contains stars but not as many as the Milky Way.

The Greeks coined the term *galaxies kuklos* for 'milky circle' when describing the Milky Way. The Milky Way was a faint band of light, but they had no idea what it was composed of. When Galileo looked at the Milky Way with the first telescope, he determined that it was made up of numerous stars.

In the late 18th century, astronomers William and Caroline Herschel mapped the distances to stars in many directions. They determined that the Milky Way was a disk-like cloud of stars with the sun near the centre.

In 1781, Charles Messier catalogued various nebulae (faint patches of light) throughout the sky and classified several of them as spiral nebulae.

In the early 20th century, astronomer Harlow Shapely measured the distributions and locations of globular star clusters. He determined that the centre of the Milky Way was 28,000 light years from Earth, near the constellations of Sagittarius and Scorpio and that the centre was a bulge, rather than a flat area.

Comets

Comets are sometimes known as cosmic snowballs. They orbit Earth in elliptical paths. A comet has four components; a nucleus, a coma, a dust tail and an iron tail. The nucleus of a comet contains the vast majority of its total mass. There are over 3000 comets found. The most famous comet is the Haley's comet. The Oort cloud is in the outer region of the solar system and contains dormant comets. Some of the comets which originate there have orbits lasting for millions of years. A great comet is a comet that you can see without using the help of a telescope. A great comet happens every 10 years. Over the course of the second half of the twentieth century, evidence provided by the orbits of comets suggested that there is not just one region of the outer Solar System producing comets, but two. The first of these regions is what is known as the Kuiper Belt, a band of comets similar in many ways to the Asteroid Belt found in the inner Solar System. Comets originating in this region have relatively short orbital periods and orbit the Sun in roughly the same plane as do the planets.

Asteroid

Asteroids are small, rocky objects that orbit the Sun. The first asteroid was Ceres, discovered by Giuseppe Piazzi in 1801. There are currently over 600,000 known asteroids in our solar system. Most asteroids are found orbiting in the Asteroid Belt, a series of rings located between the orbits of Mars and Jupiter. Asteroids are clues to the formation of the rocky planets in our solar system. The objects we see today are left over from a time when the solar system formed 4.5 billion years ago. Asteroids are not the only things that hit Earth. Each day 100 tons of objects hit Earth. Most of it is destroyed by friction. If it does hit the ground, then it is a meteorite. While asteroid impacts were more common in the past, they are not as frequent today.

Black Holes

A black hole is a region of spacetime where gravity is so strong that nothing - no particles or even electromagnetic radiation such as light - can escape from it. The theory of general relativity predicts that a sufficiently compact mass can deform spacetime to form a black hole. If black holes evaporate under Hawking radiation, a solar mass black hole will evaporate over 1064 years. A supermassive black hole with a mass of 1011 (100 billion) M ⊙ will evaporate in around 2×10100 years.
The first modern solution of general relativity that would characterize a black hole was found by Karl Schwarzschild in 1916, although its interpretation as a region of space from which nothing can escape was first published by David Finkelstein in 1958. What happens if a person gets trapped in a black hole? The gravitational field becomes so strong that not even light can escape, rendering the region where the star used to be profoundly dark: a black hole. As you go deeper into the black hole, space becomes ever curvier until, at the centre, it becomes infinitely curved.
How do Black holes die? If Hawking's theory of black hole radiation is correct,

then black holes are expected to shrink and evaporate over time as they lose mass by the emission of photons and other particles.

Quasars

A quasar is an extremely luminous active galactic nucleus, in which a supermassive black hole with mass ranging from millions to billions of times the mass of the Sun is surrounded by a gaseous accretion disk. A quasar is formed when a super massive black hole at the centre of a galaxy has enough material around it to fall into the accretion disc to generate the energy to power it. The only galaxies with enough material to create a quasar are young galaxies and colliding galaxies. They shine so brightly that they eclipse the ancient galaxies containing them. Quasars are distant objects powered by black holes, a billion times as massive as our Sun. These powerful dynamos have fascinated astronomers since their discovery half a century ago. In the 1930's, Karl Jansky, a physicist with Bell Telephone Laboratories, discovered the static interference on transatlantic phone lines was coming from the Milky Way.

By the 1950's, astronomers were using radio telescopes to probe the heavens and pairing their signals with visible examinations of the heavens.

'Quasars are thought to form in regions of the universe where the large-scale density of matter is much higher than average,' astronomer Fabian Walter, of Max Planck Institute for Astronomy, said in a statement. Most quasars have been found billions of light years away. Because it takes light time to travel, studying objects in space functions much like a time machine; we see the object as it was when light left it, billions of years ago. Thus, the further away scientists look, the further back in time they can see. Most of the more than 2000 known quasars existed in the early life of the galaxy. Galaxies like the Milky Way may have once hosted a quasar that has long been silent.

In December 2017, the most distant quasar was found sitting more than 13 billion light-years from Earth. Scientists observed the quasar, known as J1342+0928, as it appeared only 690 million years after the Big Bang. Quasars this young can reveal information about how galaxies evolved over time. They emit energies of millions, billions, or even trillions of electron volts. This energy exceeds the total of the light of all the stars within a galaxy.

White dwarf

A white dwarf, also called a degenerate dwarf, is a stellar core remnant composed mostly of electron-degenerate matter. A white dwarf is very dense; its mass is comparable to that of the Sun, while its volume is comparable to that of Earth. Stars like our sun, fuse hydrogen in their cores into helium. White dwarfs are stars that have burned up all of the hydrogen they once used as nuclear fuel. Fusion in a star's core produces heat and outward pressure, but this pressure is kept in balance by the inward push of gravity generated by a star's mass. A white dwarf takes about 4 billion years to cool to 6,000 K, so we can conclude that the cluster is around 4 billion years old. White dwarf stars are the corpses of stars. This happens once they have used up all their fuel and lack the temperature and pressure to continue fusion in their core. The star starts to collapse, but then a new shell of hydrogen fuel gets going. This causes the outer envelope of the star to puff out into a red giant. A white dwarf is what stars like the Sun become after they have exhausted their nuclear fuel. Near the end of its nuclear burning stage, this type of star expels most of its outer material, creating a planetary nebula.

Protostar

A protostar is an incredibly young star that is still gathering mass from its parent molecular cloud. The protostellar phase is the earliest one in the process of stellar evolution. For a low mass star, it lasts about 500,000 years. The protostar is the second stage of a new-born star in a nebula. A new star is born because when the nebula contracts, it becomes dense and hot and this is how a star is born and is in its first stage. The protostar is its second stage and to reach the third stage it has to be at least 15,000,000 degree Celsius. A protostar is formed as gravity begins to pull the gases together into a ball. This process is known as accretion. As gravity pulls the gasses closer to the centre of the ball, gravitational energy begins to heat them, causing the gasses to emit radiation. At first, the radiation simply escapes into space. Protostar stars begin to form from clouds of gas in space. As the cloud collapses, it begins to spin and by the time a protostar is formed, the cloud flattens and there is a protostellar disk spinning around the protostar.

Main Sequence

In astronomy, the main sequence is a continuous and distinctive band of stars that appears on plots of stellar colour versus brightness. These colour-magnitude plots are known as Hertzsprung–Russell diagrams after their co-developers, Ejnar Hertzsprung and Henry Norris Russell. Main sequence stars fuse hydrogen atoms to form helium atoms in their cores. About 90 percent of the stars in the universe, including the sun, are main sequence stars. These stars can range from about a tenth of the mass of the sun to up to 200 times as massive.

Neutron Star

A neutron star is the collapsed core of a giant star which before collapse had a total mass of between 10 and 29 solar masses. Neutron stars are the smallest and densest stars, excluding black holes and hypothetical white holes, quark stars and strange stars. They are a celestial object of exceedingly small radius (typically 30 km) and extremely high density, composed predominantly of tightly packed neutrons. Neutron stars are thought to form by the gravitational collapse of the remnant of a massive star after a supernova explosion, provided that the star is insufficiently massive to produce a black hole.

Red Giant

Red giant stars reach sizes of 100 million to 1 billion kilometres in diameter (62 million to 621 million miles), 100 to 1,000 times the size of the sun today. The Sun, and any red dwarfs above about 0.25 solar masses, will expand into what is called a red giant, a late stage of stellar evolution. At this stage, the star starts to fuse different elements, and eventually throws off its layers as a planetary nebula, leaving behind a white dwarf made of carbon and oxygen. In approximately 5 billion years, the sun will begin the helium-burning process, turning into a red giant star. When it expands, its outer layers will consume Mercury and Venus and reach Earth. When stars morph into red giants, they change the habitable zones of their system. Examples of well-known stars in the RG phase are Aldebaran (Alpha Tauri) and Mira (Omicron Ceti). More massive Main Sequence stars evolve more quickly and expand further to become Red Super Giants (RSG). Betelgeuse (Alpha Orionis) is a well-known example of an RSG. Like every other Star, a Red Giant dies when it has burned all its fuel and there is no more pressure to keep gravity pushing towards the centre. Basically, a Red Giant is formed when a Star like our Sun burns all of its hydrogen to helium and then rearranges itself. This process takes about 10 Billion years. Earth could survive a red-giant Sun. Over time, the star will change into a red giant and grow to more than 400 times its original size. As they expand, red giants engulf some of their close-orbiting planets. The outer layers of the star start to grow, cool and turn red again as it enters its second red giant phase. How many Earths can fit into a Red Giant star? Answer: You can fit 1300 Earths in a Red Giant star.

Brown Dwarf

Brown dwarfs are objects which have a size between that of a giant planet like Jupiter and that of a small star. In fact, most astronomers would classify any object with between 15 times the mass of Jupiter and 75 times the mass of Jupiter to be a brown dwarf. It is a type of substellar object that has a mass between those of the heaviest gas giant planets and the least massive stars, i.e. approximately 13 to 75–80 times that of Jupiter (M J), or approximately 2.5×1028 kg to about 1.5×1029 kg. These objects, known as brown dwarfs, have many of the elements of their more famous siblings but lack the mass needed to jumpstart nuclear fusion in their core. Because brown dwarfs never burn fusion at their core, scientists sometimes refer to them as 'failed stars.'
White dwarfs and brown dwarfs are bright enough to support habitable zones — regions around them warm enough for planets to sustain liquid water on their surfaces. As such, worlds orbiting them might be able support alien life as we know it, as there is life virtually everywhere there is water on Earth.
'We're finding that brown dwarfs are not like small stars in terms of their magnetic activity; they're like giant planets with

hugely powerful auroras,' Hallinan said in the report. 'If you were able to stand on the surface of the brown dwarf we observed – something you could never do because of its extremely hot temperatures and crushing surface gravity – you would sometimes be treated to a fantastic light show courtesy of auroras hundreds of thousands of times more powerful than any detected in our solar system.'

Luminous blue variable

Luminous blue variables are massive evolved stars that show unpredictable and sometimes dramatic variations in both their spectra and brightness. They are also known as S Doradus variables after S Doradus, one of the brightest stars of the Large Magellanic Cloud. Luminous Blue Variables (LBVs) are the most luminous variable blue stars, showing moderate (0.5--2 mag) light changes on timescales of decades apparently at constant bolometric luminosity. LBVs are considered to be at an intermediate stage between massive O stars and W-R stars in which the outer layers are removed by extreme mass-loss. The LBV definition is overly broad and includes the S Dor, P Cygni type and Hubble-Sandage variables, with around a dozen LBVs are currently known in the Galaxy and LMC and around 20 further afield. LBVs lie close to the Humphreys-Davidson instability limit (Humphreys & Davidson 1979), which is an observed luminosity cut off above which red supergiants are not found. The LBV variability has therefore been linked to the instability which allows the most massive stars to lose sufficient mass to prevent them from becoming a red supergiant. Although the mechanism for this instability remains poorly known.

G-type main-sequence star

A G-type main-sequence star (Spectral type: G-V), often (and imprecisely) called a yellow dwarf, or G dwarf star, is a main-sequence star (luminosity class V) of spectral type G. Such a star has about 0.84 to 1.15 solar masses and surface temperature of between 5,300 and 6,000 K. How many G-type stars are there? As many as 512 or more stars of spectral type 'G' (not including white dwarf stellar remnants) are currently believed to be located within 100 light-years or (or 30.7 parsecs) of Sol - including Sol itself. A G-type main-sequence star will fuse hydrogen for approximately 10 billion years, until it is exhausted at the centre of the star.

K-type main-sequence star

A K-type main-sequence star, also referred to as a K dwarf or Orange dwarf, is a main-sequence (hydrogen-burning) star of spectral type K and luminosity class V. These stars are intermediate in size between red M-type main-sequence stars (red dwarfs) and yellow G-type main-sequence stars. K-type dwarf stars are dimmer than the Sun but brighter than the faintest stars. These stars live an exceptionally long time – 17 billion to 70 billion years, compared to 10 billion years for the Sun – giving plenty of time for life to evolve.

Supergiant star

Supergiant's are among the most massive and most luminous stars. Supergiant stars occupy the top region of the Hertzsprung–Russell diagram with absolute visual magnitudes between about −3 and −8. The temperature range of supergiant stars spans from about 3,450 K to over 20,000 K.

Hyper giant star

A hypergiant is an exceedingly rare kind of star that has an extremely high luminosity and mass loss by stellar winds. The term hypergiant is defined as luminosity class 0 in the MKK system.

Scientists who changed the way we understand the world

Albert Einstein - Found the theory of relativity

Isaac Newton – Found the theory of gravity

Karl Schwarzschild – Found black holes

Stephen Hawking – Black holes emit radiation

Marie Curie – Radium and polonium

Rosalind Franklin - X-ray diffraction

Galileo Galei – Milky Way

Charles Darwin – Evolution

Nicolaus Copernicus – Made a model of the universe but with the Sun at the centre

Blazar

First of all, what is a blazar? A blazar is a region at the centre of a galaxy that emits extremely powerful jets of radiation in the direction of the Earth. A blazar is a feeding super-massive black-hole (SMBH) in the heart of a distant galaxy that produces a high-energy jet, viewed face-on from Earth. Like other forms of active galactic nuclei (AGN), blazars are the most luminous and energetic objects in the known universe.

Supercluster

The supercluster we live in is known as the Virgo Supercluster. It is an enormous collection of more than a million galaxies, stretching across a region of space 110 million light-years across. Our Sun is just one member of the Milky Way and the Milky Way is part of a collection of galaxies known as the Local Group. The supercluster is about 500 million light years across as well as the local group is estimated 10 million light years apart. The local group houses a staggering 54 galaxies. It is estimated that in the observable universe there are 10 million superclusters.

Wormholes

If you saw a wormhole in reality it would appear round and spherical, a bit like a black hole. Light from the other side passes through and gives you a window to a faraway place. But are wormholes real or are they disguised as physics and maths? If they are real, how do they work and where do we find them?

Throughout human history, we thought space was simple. Einstein's theory of relativity says that space and time make space together and that they are not the same everywhere. Our universe is like a big flat sheet and bent just the right way. Wormholes could connect distant places with a short bridge which could be crossed, almost instantaneously enabling you to travel the universe, even faster than the speed of light. So where can you find a wormhole? Possibly only on paper. General relativity says it might be possible but that means it does not have to exist. General relativity is a mathematical theory. It is a set of equations that have many possible answers. Not all maths describes relativity. But they are theoretically possible. The first kind of wormholes to be theorised were Einstein Rosen Bridges. They described every black hole as a sort of portal to an infinite parallel universe.

500 facts about Space

1. Earth is the only planet ever found with life. Scientists are trying really hard to search for new planets because of their prediction that the Sun is going to become bigger and expand and will destroy the Earth.

2. The Sun is the nearest star in the solar system. Our Sun is a G-type main sequence star.

3. The largest planet in the solar system is Jupiter. 1300 Earths could fit into Jupiter.

4. The Milky Way is a spiral galaxy.

5. Space is completely silent. There are no sounds in Space.

6. The hottest planet in our solar system is Venus. Venus is 450 degrees and is not the closest planet to the Sun. Mercury is the hottest planet to the Sun but does not trap heat.

7. Mercury does not have an atmosphere.

8. Mercury has a thin exosphere made up of atoms blasted off the surface by the solar wind and striking meteoroids.

9. A full NASA space suit costs $12,000,000. That is 12 million dollars.

10. It is estimated that there are more than 200 billion stars in the milk way. This is an estimate by scientists.

11. The footprints of people on the moon will be there for 100 million years. There is no water or wind to remove the footprints.

12. One day on Venus is actually longer than a year on Venus. A day on Venus is 245 days and a year on Venus is 225 Earth days.

13. If two same types of material will touch in space, they will be bonded together.

14. There is water floating in Space. Astronomers found a floating water vapour which holds 140 million times the mass in the Earth's ocean.

This was a large discovery because it was 10 billion light years away.

15. There is a volcano on Mars which is three times the size of Mount Everest. Olympus Mons is the volcano on Mars.

16. The moon was actually a piece of the Earth.

17. When Earth was really young it was struck by a giant object and the piece we call the Moon got separated from the Earth.

18. The largest asteroid is 965 km wide or 600 mi. wide.

19. There are four types of spiral galaxies: Spiral, Barrell Spiral, Elliptical and Irregular. Our galaxy is a spiral galaxy.

20. Neutron stars can spin 600 times a second.

21. Pluto was a planet but it is now a dwarf planet. It was demoted on August 2006 because it did not meet the three criteria the IAU uses to define a full-sized planet.

22. Essentially Pluto meets all the criteria to be a planet except one - it 'has not cleared its neighbouring region of other objects.'

23. Mercury and Venus are the only planets in our solar system that do not have moons.

24. If a star comes too close to a black hole it can rip apart.

25. Our solar system is 4.571 billion years old.

26. The Earth is 4.543 billion years old.

27. The Milky Way is 13.51 billion years old.

28. The moon is 4.53 billion years old.

29. Andromeda galaxy is a spiral galaxy.

30. Andromeda and the Milky Way will collide in 4.5 billion years and become an elliptical galaxy.

31. One million Earths could fit inside the sun.

32. Recently, NASA revealed its strongest evidence yet that there is intermittent running water on Mars.

33. You wouldn't be able to walk on Jupiter, Saturn, Uranus, or Neptune because they have no solid surface.

34. An asteroid enters the Earth's atmosphere every year, but it gets destroyed before it lands.

35. Meteorites are rocks from an asteroid that manages to land into the Earth's surface before getting crushed.

36. There are more stars in the universe than grains of sand on all of the beaches. That is at least a billion trillion.

37. The sunset on Mars appears blue.

38. Earth is the only planet not named after a god.

Mercury - Messenger for Roman gods
Venus – Goddess of love and beauty
Mars – God of war, called *Ares* by Greeks
Jupiter – King of the Gods (*Zeus*)
Saturn - Roman god of time
Uranus - Greek god of sky (*Herschel*)
Neptune - God of the sea (*Poseidon*)

39. A quasar lasts from ten million to a few billion years.

40. The flattest star ever found in the universe is Archener.

41. The largest star in the universe ever found is VY Majoris.

42. We have discovered 8 planets and 5 dwarf planets.

43. There are 4000 exoplanets discovered and confirmed.

44. A nebula can range in size from millions of miles across to hundreds of light years across.

45. A protostar becomes a main sequence star when its core temperature exceeds 10 million (10,000,000) K.

46. A Protostar's estimated temperature is 2000 to 3000 K.

47. The universe is filled with invisible stuff.

48. Dark matter is invisible. It was found by Fritz Zwicky.

49. The universe has echoes of its birth.

50. There may be more universes. This is a prediction or an estimate.

51. If you unravelled all of the DNA in your body, it would span 34 billion miles, reaching to Pluto (2.66 billion miles away) and back six times.

52. In fact, your body contains cosmic relics from the creation of the universe. Almost all of your hydrogen atoms were formed in the Big Bang, about 13.7 billion years ago.

53. Space isn't always cold.

54. NASA has recorded eerie space sounds in Space.

55. It is really expensive to load something into space.

56. The international space station (ISS) is the size of a football pitch.

57. If you didn't have a spacesuit, you would last about 15 seconds.

58. The sun makes up 99.8% of the solar system's mass.

59. The centre of the Milky Way galaxy has tens of thousands of black holes.

60. Comets are leftovers from the creation of our solar system about 4.5 billion years ago - they consist of sand, ice and carbon dioxide.

61. There may be life on Mars.

62. Halley's comet won't orbit Earth until 2061.

63. We are nowhere near the centre of the galaxy.

64. There are more than 200 moons in our solar system.

65. The temperature in the void of space is about −270.45 °C.

66. Spacecraft have visited all the known planets in our solar system.

67. The universe is expanding since its formation in the Big Bang.

68. There are 100-400 billion stars in our galaxy.

69. Olympus Mons, the volcano on Mars, is three times bigger than Mount Everest.

70. Mars has two small moons, *Phobos* and *Deimos*. They were discovered in 1877 by astronomer Asaph Hall, who named them the Latin terms for 'fear' and 'panic'.

71. Galileo Galilei discovered our galaxy called the Milky Way.

72. Edwin Hubble discovered the galaxy called Andromeda.

73. We don't know who discovered the planet Mercury. It was first observed by astronomers Galileo Galilei and Thomas Harriot.

74. Galileo Galilei discovered the planet called Venus in 1610.

75. Galileo Galilei also discovered the planets called Mars, Jupiter and Saturn.

76. William Herschel discovered the planet called Uranus.

77. Urbain Le Verrier, John Couch Adams and Johann Gottfried Galle all discovered Neptune. Neptune was supposedly discovered in 1846 by Johann Gottfried Galle using calculations by Urbain Le Verrier and John Couch Adams, making it a joint British-French-German discovery. But these astronomers were not the first to observe Neptune. That honor goes to the famous Italian astronomer Galileo Galilei.

78. Outer space is not empty.

79. Uranus is tilted on its side.

80. Jupiter's moon Io has towering volcanic eruptions.

81. Venus has super powerful winds. At the very top of the cloud layers on Venus, wind speeds reach 355 km/hour (or 100 meters/second). This is the same as the jet stream here

on Earth. As you descend through the cloud layers though, the wind speeds pick up. In the middle layer, the winds can reach speeds of more than 700 km/hour.

82. It rains sulfric acid on Venus. This could kill you in moments.

83. There is water and ice everywhere but scientists weren't looking in the right places to find them.

84. There could be life in the solar system anywhere. Scientists are continuously searching for life everywhere.

85. Mercury is still shrinking; its size is getting smaller.

86. There are mountains on Pluto. NASA's New Horizons spacecraft flew by there in 2015, sending back pictures that altered our view of Pluto forever. Among the astounding discoveries were icy mountains that are 11,000 feet (3,300 meters) high, indicating that Pluto must have been geologically active as little as 100 million years ago. But geological activity requires energy and the

source of that energy inside Pluto is a mystery. The sun is too far away from Pluto to generate enough heat for geological activity and there are no large planets nearby that could have caused such disruption with gravity.

87. It would take nine years to walk to the moon.

88. Stepping off the lunar landing module Eagle, astronaut Neil Armstrong became the first human to walk on the surface of the moon.

89. On July 20 1969, at 10:56 p.m. and 240,000 miles away from Earth, Neil Armstrong, spoke to more than a billion people listening at home: 'That's one small step for man, one giant leap for mankind.'

90. If you can spot the Andromeda Galaxy with your naked eyes, you can see something 14.7 billion miles away.

91. Jupiter has 79 moons.

92. Enceladus, one of Saturn's smaller moons, reflects 90% of the Sun's light.

93. The whirlpool galaxy is the first galaxy identified as a spiral galaxy.

94. Our Sun weighs 330,000 times more than the Earth.

95. Our galaxy is 105,700 light years wide.

96. On Mars there are lower gravity than Earth because it would be 37.83% of your weight on Earth. You can jump three times higher on Mars than Earth.

97. NASA's Crater Observation and Sensing Satellite (LCROSS) found evidence of water on the Earth's Moon.

98. The Sun makes a full rotation once every 25 to 35 days.

99. Due to the Sun and Moon's gravitational pull, we have tides.

100. According to mathematics, white holes are possible, although as of yet we have found none.

101. The glow on Uranus is because of the gases in its atmosphere.

102. In our solar system there are 4 planets known as gas giants: Jupiter, Saturn, Uranus and Neptune.

103. Due to the tilt on Uranus, a season on Uranus is 21 Earth years.

104. Neptune's moon, Triton, orbits the planet backwards.

105. Triton is getting closer to the planet it orbits.

106. Neptune takes nearly 165 earth years to make one orbit.

107. The largest moon on Pluto, Charon, is the half size of Pluto.

108. A day on Pluto lasts 153.6 hours long.

109. Mercury is the smallest planet in the solar system.

110. Saturn is the second largest planet in the solar system.

111. Any free-moving liquid in outer space will form itself into a sphere.

112. Mercury, Venus, Earth and Mars are known as the 'Inner Planets'.

113. Light travels from the Sun to the Earth in less than ten minutes.

114. The Black Arrow is the only British satellite to be launched using a British rocket.

115. We know more about Mars and the moon than we know about the oceans.

116. Only 5% of the universe is visible from the Earth.

117. At any given moment, there are at least 2,000 thunderstorms happening on Earth.

118. The rotation of the Earth is slowing down as time goes on.

119. The first artificial satellite in space was called 'Sputnik'.

120. Our moon is moving away from Earth at a rate of 1.6 inches (4 cm) per year.

121. Saturn is the only planet that could float in water. Saturn is the lightest planet.

122. Astronauts can't burp in space.

123. The planet Uranus was called 'George's star'.

124. Outer space is only 62 miles away from inner space.

125. The weight of the Earth is 81 times bigger than the weight on the Moon.

126. The International Space Station (ISS) circles the Earth every 1 hour and 32 minutes.

127. Stars twinkle because of the way light is disrupted as it passes through Earth's atmosphere.

128. We always see the same side of the Moon, no matter where we stand on Earth.

129. With the naked eye, you can see 3 to 7 different galaxies from the Earth.

130. In 2016, scientists detected a radio signal from a source 5 billion light-years away.

131. Andromeda galaxy is 2.5 million light years away from the Milky Way.

132. The first supernova observed outside of our own galaxy was in 1885.

133. The first black hole ever photographed is 3 million (3,000,000) times the size of the Earth.

134. The second man to ever step foot on the Moon was Buzz Aldrin. He named it the Moon because the maiden name of his mother was Moon.

135. The birth name of Buzz Aldrin was Edwin Eugene Aldrin Jr.

136. It snows metal on Venus.

137. In 1974, the first spacecraft to visit Mercury was The Mariner 10. It

managed to photograph 45% of Mercury's surface.

138. The first ever soft drink in Space was Coca-Cola.

139. Astronomers who go to space can grow up to 5cm taller. This tallness will go when you re-enter the Earth's atmosphere.

140. The first woman to ever go into space was a Russian woman called Valentina Tereshkova.

141. If the rings of Saturn were three feet long, then they would be 10,000 times thinner than a razorblade.

142. In space suits there is a Velcro patch to help astronauts itch.

143. Asteroids are the by-products of formations in the solar system more than 4 billion years ago.

144. The first animal to go to space was a dog called Laika on the Soviet spacecraft Sputnik 2 on 3 November 1957.

145. The real meaning of astronaut is star finder.

146. NASA stands for National Aeronautics Space Administration.

147. Gennady Paldalka has spent the most time in Space.

148. In China, the Milky Way is known as the 'Silver River'.

149. Red dwarf stars that are low in mass can burn up to 10 trillion years.

150. A large percentage of asteroids are pulled in by Jupiter's gravity.

151. If you want to use a pen in space, it won't work.

152. On average, it takes light only 1.3 seconds to get from the Moon to the Earth.

153. There are 88 recognised star constellations in our night sky.

154. The centre of the comet is called a nucleus.

155. There is a planet half the radius of the Earth with a surface made up of diamonds.

156. Our moon would fit between Earth and the Moon 221 times.

157. Kepler-452b is a planet just like Earth.

158. A galaxy is a massive group of stars, star clusters, interstellar gas, dust, and dark matter which is all gravitationally bound together.

159. There are potentially more than 170 billion galaxies in the observable universe.

160. Mars is also called the 'Red Planet'.

161. Two golden orb spiders were flown into space. They reacted different. Their webs looked much like webs spun on Earth, though in space the webs were more circular.

162. On June 14, 1949, the first monkey to be sent successfully into Space was Albert II. The monkey was a rhesus monkey whose flight made it to a height of 134 km high (83 miles).

163. If the Sun would be the size of a door, then Earth would be the size of a nickel.

164. There is an asteroid that has rings like Saturn. The asteroid's name is a Cariklo.

165. There is a planet made out of diamonds that is the twice the size of Earth.

166. There are more trees on Earth than there are stars in the Milky Way.

167. Space is full of space junk.

168. There is a reason why Space is dark even though there are lots of stars. This phenomenon is known as Olbers' Paradox, named for the German astronomer Heinrich Wilhelm Olbers who posed it in 1823: 'If the universe is infinite, static and timeless, then everywhere you look should eventually hit a star'.

169. Dinosaurs became extinct because of a comet, asteroid or meteorite impact.

170. The universe approximately contains over 100 billion galaxies.

171. The skin on your feet peels off when you are in Space.

172. Tears in your eyes would not fall down in Space because of loss of gravity.

173. Kepler-78b is referred as the 'lava world'.

174. The sun travels around the Milky Way once every 200 million years - a journey of 100,000 light years.

175. The only planet that can spin backwards is Venus.

176. Uranus is the only planet that has 27 moons.

177. The planet with the most moons in our galaxy is Jupiter.

178. An Astronomical Unit is used to measure the distance between the Earth and the Sun.

179. The biggest black hole is the Monster Black Hole.

180. The Sun is white, not yellow.

181. The planet Saturn's rings are not in the solid state.

182. Mercury is the fastest planet in the Solar System.

183. The largest canyon system in the solar system is Valles Marineras on Mars. It's more than 4,000 kilometres (3,000 miles) long - enough to stretch from California to New York. It is nine times as long and four times as deep as Earth's Grand Canyon.

184. Comets are sometimes referred to as 'dirty snowballs' or 'cosmic snowballs.'

185. A comet has four components: a nucleus, a coma, a dust tail and an ion tail.

186. Comets orbit the Sun just like the planets.

187. A great comet is one which is bright enough to be visible from Earth without the need for a telescope.

188. Approximately one great comet happens every ten years.

189. The difference between a meteor and meteorite is that a meteor enters the Earth's atmosphere but gets destroyed and a meteorite is a piece of the meteor that succeeds getting into the Earth's atmosphere.

190. A meteoroid is rocky or iron debris floating in space.

191. Most of the gold on earth was delivered through meteorite impacts more than 3.8 billion years ago.

192. The Willamette meteorite is the largest meteorite ever found.

193. The lunar module, Eagle, was so small that there was no room for seats. While Eagle dropped 60 miles to the moon's surface, Neil Armstrong and Buzz Aldrin had to stand up.

194. Gravity on the Moon is only one-sixth as strong as gravity on Earth. If you jumped on the Moon, you'd go six times higher.

195. The universe has the same temperature everywhere.

196. The Sun is producing only a third of the neutrinos expected.

197. The first gravitational waves detected came from a binary black hole system nobody predicted.

198. Most of the planetary systems are actually different to ours.

199. Most of the stuff in the universe is repulsive gravity.

200. The International Space Station is the most expensive object ever made by humans. It has cost 150 billion dollars so far.

201. If the earth were as large as a sand grain, the sun would be as large as an orange.

202. If you could fold a piece of paper 42 times, that piece of paper would be thick enough to be able to reach the Moon.

203. On Jupiter and Saturn it rains diamonds.

204. It is a myth that you can see the wall of China from space.

205. During a solar eclipse, it appears to observers on Earth as if the Sun and Moon were exactly the same size. However, this is only a huge coincidence, because the Sun is 400 times as big as the Moon, but also 400 times further away.

206. 2016 was one second longer than 2015.

207. The Earth is the only planet where a fire can burn something or someone. The other planets do not have oxygen for it to happen.

208. During the first few days in space, astronauts often suffer from space sickness because of the weightlessness and their sense of balance is impaired. Important tasks such as outboard work are not carried out in the first days of a space mission.

209. NASA (National Aeronautics Space Administration) is attempting to

answer the question if we are alone in the universe.

210. Three men from Yemen accused NASA of 'settling' on Mars. According to the men, their ancestors gave it to them 3,000 years ago.

211. If you hold a grain of sand against the night sky, it will hide 10,000 galaxies from your eyes. Weird, but true.

212. If you could drive directly to the Moon by car at a speed of 80 miles per hour, it would take about four months to reach it.

213. Neptune, Saturn and Venus are the names of three seaside resorts in Romania.

214. The ISS orbits the Earth at a speed of 4.76 miles per second.

215. Hot Neptune is a planet's name that is 10,800 degrees Fahrenheit.

216. It may be dangerous to leave the Earth in a spaceship because the Earth is surrounded by so much

space debris. This is also known as the Kessler syndrome.

217. Astronauts in the ISS can witness 15 sunrises and 15 sunsets a day.

218. Jupiter is 318 times bigger than Earth.

219. Uranus is 63 times bigger than Earth.

220. When the Big Bang theory was presented for the first time scientifically, it was rejected by many scientists because it seemed too religious.

221. Due to strong solar storms in 1859, the earth experienced the strongest geomagnetic storm ever recorded.

222. There is a large dark spot at the North Pole of Pluto's moon Charon, and scientists have no idea what it is. They therefore called it *Mordor,* in reference to the mysterious dark land in 'The Lord of the Rings'.

223. All of our school textbooks show the solar system with the planets close enough to fit on one page. In actuality if you were to draw the

solar system to scale and the earth was the size of a pea on paper, Jupiter would be over 984 feet away and Pluto would be one and a half miles away. The nearest star would be 9,940 miles away on paper.

224. If the earth was the size of a billiard ball, it would be smoother than one.

225. The highest point on Earth is Mount Everest and the deepest is the Mariana Trench.

226. Venus rotates around its own axis at only four miles per hour. So you could walk around Venus faster than it can turn itself.

227. If you were able to fold a piece of paper a total of 102 times, it would be about as thick as the entire known universe.

228. In the next six years, NASA plans to grow crops on the moon.

229. NASA wants to send a probe to Uranus within the next 15 years.

230. Russia has more land mass than Pluto.

231. Michael James Massimino, an astronaut who has made several guest appearances in *The Big Bang Theory*, was the first person to tweet from space.

232. If you were to stack all the viruses in the world on top of each other, this would result in a tower that would extend far beyond the moon, even further than our sun, further than Alpha Centauri and further than the edge of the Milky Way and into the next galaxy, with a total height of about 200 million light years.

233. The planet Uranus was discovered in 1781, while the Antarctic was not discovered until 1820.

234. In the 1880s, Charles Pickering, director of the Harvard Observatory, was constantly complaining about his male colleagues. One day he supposedly said that even his Scottish maid would be able to perform better. He decided to hire his housekeeper Williamina Fleming, who then went on to successfully lead a team for several decades, helping to classify thousands of stars.

She even discovered a white dwarf and was the first human to find the Horsehead Nebula.

235. NASA has special wristwatches produced for some of its employees that show the time of day on Mars.

236. The 'Fallen Astronaut Sculpture' is the only work of art on the moon so far. It was created by Belgian artist Paul Van Haydock and brought to the moon during the Apollo 15 mission in 1971. It commemorates the 14 astronauts who died prior to the Apollo 15 mission.

237. The Kennedy Space Centre in Cape Canaveral is located at exactly 28 degrees north latitude, as the Moon's orbit is also rotated by 28 degrees relative to the equator. When flying to the Moon, you therefore receive maximum momentum from the earth's rotation.

238. NASA has two identical satellites orbiting the Earth and repeatedly measuring the distance between each other to detect gravitational deviations. They are nicknamed *Tom*

and *Jerry* because one satellite is always 'chasing' the other.

239. It takes eight minutes and 17 seconds until the light from the sun reaches the earth.

240. Asia has a larger surface area than the Moon. While the surface of the Moon measures only 14,645,698 square miles, Asia covers a total of 17,212,368 square miles.

241. On the 18th of October 1963, French scientists launched a rocket to move the first cat into space. The feline's name was Felicitate and she landed safely on the ground after a parachute descent.

242. Scientists are always trying to re-create the Big Bang on a small scale in great big labs to learn more about the Universe.

243. After three minutes of the Big Bang, the Universe had already formed gravity.

244. If you were travelling at almost 20,000 kilometres per hour on a space shuttle it would still take 165

thousand years just to reach the closest star in our galaxy.

245. When you are looking at stars in the galaxy, you are looking into the past.

246. Life can begin and stay alive in freezing conditions and also in extremely hot conditions.

247. Scientists are trying to find ways of fuelling spacecraft using antimatter.

248. Black holes can be extremely big or extremely small.

249. Scientists are sure that there is a Super Massive Black Hole at the centre of the Milky Way galaxy.

250. Scientists believe that black holes eventually die out.

251. Gamma radiation can be recreated on earth through nuclear fusion.

252. Gamma rays can produce energy that is over 1 million times more that the energy of the sun.

253. Gamma ray bursts could occur anywhere in the universe at any time.

254. Total solar eclipses can last up to 8 minutes.

255. Lunar eclipses can last for hours.

256. The nearest known quasar to Earth is 780 million light years away.

257. All quasars have a life cycle and will die out.

258. Over 190 thousand quasars have been discovered since the 1950's.

259. Light and wave lengths from the Andromeda galaxy are Blueshifts.

260. The Sun formed in a nebula.

261. The atmosphere on Mercury is very thin producing no weather.

262. The atmosphere on Earth is very thick producing mixed weather.

263. Voyager 1 moves at a speed of 11 miles per second.

264. Voyager 2 moves at a speed of 9.5 miles per second.

265. NASA is located in Washington D.C.

266. More than 100 asteroids are known to have orbiting moons.

267. Comet sizes range from 1 mile to 300 miles.

268. The larges supercluster is actually 60 times larger than the Milky Way.

269. Before space exploration, humans did not know about the solar system. They thought that the Earth was at the centre of the universe.

270. Before, people thought the Earth was flat. When Aristotle claimed that the Earth was round, he showed his proof.
   a. Ships appear from behind the horizon sails first, then the hull.
   b. From a higher standpoint you can see further.
   c. A lunar eclipse is caused by the Earth's shadow and this shadow is always circular.
   d. If you travel south you see new constellations above the southern horizon and you see Polaris lower and lower the more you travel south.

271. The asteroid belt is located between Mars and Jupiter.

272. The forming of a new star in a galaxy at an amazingly fast pace is called a Starburst.

273. When you see the grey speckles of static on your TV when the channels are not working, that static is directly a cause of the Big Bang.

274. If a star is really large after its birth, the star will live for less time as a smaller star.

275. Brown dwarfs are actually failed stars.

276. The Sun is a yellow dwarf (G type – Main sequence star).

277. The star Pollux is an orange star.

278. The Sun eventually becomes a red giant.

279. Blue supergiant's have short life spans and are rare compared to other stars.

280. Blue hypergiants are extremely luminous.

281. The largest red supergiant star ever known is 1800 times bigger than the Sun.

282. Red Hypergiants produce 66,000 times more than the Sun.

283. Neutron stars are so dense that a teaspoon of their matter weighs millions of tons.

284. The Sun's official name is 'Sol'.

285. Pulsars spin from 5,000 to 40,000 times per minute.

286. The neutron stars are actually 2 trillion times more magnetic than the Earth.

287. The magnetars are 1000 times more magnetic than the neutron stars.

288. Pulsars slow down as they age.

289. Jocelyn Bell Burnell invented Neutron Stars.

290. Some Neutron stars emit electromagnetic radiation so you can see them like pulsars.

291. Dame Jocelyn Bell Burnell discovered Pulsars.

292. Mars has 2 moons.

293. Earth has 1 Moon.

294. Earth does not have any rings.

295. Venus does not have any rings.

296. Mars does not have any rings.

297. Jupiter has 4 rings.

298. Saturn is the least dense planet in the solar system.

299. The Hubble Space Telescope receives its energy from the Sun through two large solar panels specially built to the telescope.

300. The James Webb Telescope is the most powerful telescope in the world.

301. The James Webb Telescope is 100 times more powerful than the Hubble Space Telescope.

302. The first mission to a comet by an unmanned spacecraft happened in 2014. The mission was called 'The Rosetta Mission'.

303. Unmanned spacecraft Voyager 1 has been in space for nearly 40 years (39 years to be exact) and is expected to last in space for at least another 10 years. The voyage was only meant to last for 5 years.

304. Astronauts need to train for 2 years straight after being selected for the program.

305. To become an astronaut with NASA, you need to become a U.S. citizen.

306. Black holes can be extremely big or extremely small.

307. Total solar eclipses can last up to 8 minutes.

308. A total lunar eclipse happens when the sun, Earth and Moon are lined up perfectly.

309. There have been two space flight disasters in NASA's history. Space Shuttle Challenger in 1986 and Space Shuttle Columbia in 2003.

310. Cosmonaut Gehrman Titov is the youngest person ever to go to space.

311. The rover spacecraft has only been on two surfaces in the solar system; the Moon and Mars.

312. Jupiter's moon, Ganymede, is the largest moon in the solar system.

313. Space starts at 62 miles above Earth.

314. NASA selects candidates to be astronauts every single 2 years.

315. The total world budget for space exploration is over a staggering 40 trillion dollars a year.

316. Quasars are brighter than the light from multiple galaxies combined.

317. The Large Hadron Collider is the largest machine in the world.

318. The Large Hadron Collider cost over $6,000,000 to complete.

319. CERN generates heat that is hotter than the sun.

320. Redshifts are in red colour.

321. Blueshifts are in blue colour.

322. Scientist Edwin Hubble has been credited with further confirming the Redshift phenomenon through extensive study now known as Hubble's Law.

323. Light and wave lengths from the Andromeda galaxy are Blueshifts.

324. Space Junk has existed since the late 1950's.

325. If Space Junk is not cleared up, we could be trapped on the Earth in the future, making it extremely difficult for space travel.

326. The Voyager probes were manufactured by Jet Propulsion Laboratories.

327. The launch site of the Voyager probes is NASA Cape Canaveral in Florida.

328. Various space agencies are working on different ways to clear up Space Junk.

329. The World Wide Web was founded at CERN.

330. CERN stands for European Organization for Nuclear Research.

331. CNSR stands for Comet Nucleus Sample Return.

332. COBE stands for Cosmic Background Explorer.

333. COMPTEL stands for Compton Telescope.

334. COSTAR stands Corrective Optics Space Telescope Axial Replacement.

335. LM stands for Apollo Lunar Module.

336. A&A stands for Astronomy and Astrophysics.

337. GOES stands for Geostationary Orbiting Environmental Satellite.

338. GOX stands for Gaseous Oxygen.

339. MRSR stands for Mars Rover and Sample Return.

340. MRSRM stands for Mars Rover and Sample Return Mission.

341. MPEC stands for Minor Planets Electronic Circular.

342. MCO stands for Mars Climate Orbiter.

343. MODIS stands for Moderate Resolution Imaging Spectroradiometer.

344. MOLA stands for Mars Observer Laser Altimeter.

345. Space is incomprehensible to the human brain.

346. Gamma rays release more energy in 10 seconds than our Sun will in 10 billion years.

347. Astronauts need to go to the toilet in every 2 hours because of a physiological response in the kidneys due zero gravity.

348. 1 light year is equal to 9.5 trillion kilometres.

349. Mars appears red in colour because it is covered in rust.

350. Venus and Uranus only rotate backwards.

351. You can put all the planets inside Jupiter and they would fit.

352. Gliese 436 b is covered burning ice. It is so close to its star that it maintains a constant temperature of more than 400 degrees Celsius. While gravity is so powerful it compresses all the water vapour in the atmosphere into a solar sheet of burning hot ice.

353. Jupiter has an enormous hurricane style storm that has been raging on its surface. It is so large that you can fit three Earths in it.

354. You can fit 1000 Jupiters into the Sun.

355. If you fart in space it won't go anywhere, especially the smell. If you

were on Earth because there is atmosphere it would go, but in space it won't.

356. Only 5% of the universe is made up of normal matter. 25% is dark matter and 70% is dark energy.

357. There are about 3 atoms per cubic metre of space.

358. The pistol star is 10 million times brighter than the Sun.

359. The pistol star is the most luminous star ever known.

360. Every year the Moon is moving away from Earth by 3.8 cm.

361. 90.99% of all the normal matter in the universe is hydrogen.

362. A full Moon is nine times brighter than a half Moon.

363. There are approximately 3,500 astronomers in the USA, but there are over 15,000 astrologers.

364. Proxima Centauri is the nearest star after Earth.

365. The temperature on Venus can rise up to 430 degrees and drop down to -140 degrees.

366. A new star is born in our galaxy roughly every 18 days.

367. A dwarf star is so dense that it takes 8 people to lift a teaspoon of its matter.

368. The planet Venus does not tilt when it orbits around the Sun, so it does not have any seasons.

369. A cosmic year is about 225 million years.

370. The cosmic year is the amount of time it takes the Sun to revolve around the centre of the Milky Way.

371. It takes Neptune about 165 years to orbit the Earth.

372. A space vehicle must move at a speed of 27.35 km (17 miles) per second to escape Earth's gravity.

373. The known cosmos contains approximately 50,000,000,000 (50 trillion) galaxies.

374. The furthest galaxies in the universe are speeding away from us at the speed of 90% of the speed of light.

375. The coldest place in the solar system is on Earth. It is Wolfgang Ketterle's lab in Massachusetts. The temperature is 0.000000000001.

376. The closest black hole is only 1600 light-years away.

377. The largest structure found in the universe is the Sloan Great Wall.

378. Saturn's moon Titan has plenty of evidence of organic (life) chemicals in its atmosphere.

379. Life is known to exist only on Earth, but in 1986 NASA found what they thought might be fossils of microscopic living things in a rock from Mars.

380. Oxygen is circulated around the helmet in space suits in order to prevent the visor from misting.

381. The pull of gravity is calculated when you multiply their masses together and then divide the total by the square of the distance between them.

382. Glowing nebulae are named so because they give off a dim, red light, as the hydrogen gas in them is heated by radiation from the nearby stars.

383. The Drake Equation was proposed by astronomer Frank Drake to work out how many civilizations there could be in our galaxy - and the figure is in millions.

384. SETI is the Search for Extra-terrestrial Intelligence - the program that analyses radio signals from space for signs of intelligent life.

385. The Milky Way galaxy is whirling rapidly, spinning our sun and all its other stars at around 100 million km per hour.

386. The Universe may have neither a centre nor an edge, because according to Einstein's theory of

relativity, gravity bends all of space time around into an endless curve.

387. Nicolaus Copernicus was the astronomer who first suggested that the Sun was at the centre of the Universe and that the Earth went round the Sun.

388. The ideas of Copernicus came not from looking at the night sky, but from studying ancient astronomy.

389. The brightest star in each constellation is called the Alpha Star and the next brightest, Beta.

390. The distance to the planets is measured by bouncing radar signals off them and timing how long the signals take to get there and back.

391. A comet's tail is made as it nears the Sun and begins to melt. A vast plume of gas millions of kilometres across is blown out behind by the solar wind. The tail is what you see, shining as the sunlight catches it.

392. The Shoemaker-Levy 9 comet smashed into Jupiter in July 1994,

with the biggest crash ever witnessed.

393. The lower a satellite's orbit, the faster it must fly to avoid falling back to the Earth. Most satellites fly in low orbits, 300 km from the earth.

394. Giant stars have burned all their hydrogen and so burn helium, fusing helium atoms to make carbon.

395. During the Moon landing, a mirror was left on the Moon's surface to reflect a laser beam which measured the Moon's distance from the Earth with amazing accuracy.

396. Spacecrafts have double hulls (outer coverings) which protect them from other space objects that crash into them.

397. From the Moon, astronauts brought back 380 kg of Moon rock.

398. Robert Goddard launched the very first liquid-fuel rocket in 1926.

399. Over 100 artificial satellites are now launched into Space every year, a few of which are Space telescopes.

400. The first rockets were made 1,000 years ago in China.

401. Planets have a magnetic field around them because of the liquid iron in their cores. As the planets rotate, so the iron swirls, generating electric currents that create the magnetic field.

402. Earth's atmosphere is the only atmosphere discovered to date that humans can breathe in.

403. Hubble's law showed that universe is getting bigger and so must have started exceedingly small. This led to the idea of The Big Bang.

404. The first astronomers thought the regular pulses from far space might be signals from aliens and pulsars were jokingly called LGMs (Little Green Men).

405. Since the star Deneb is 1800 light years away, we see it as it was when the emperor Septimius Severus was ruling Rome (AD 200).

406. With powerful telescopes, astronomers can see galaxies 2 billion light years away. This means we see them as they were when the only life forms on Earth were bacteria.

407. Uranus's moon Miranda is the weirdest moon of all. It seems to have been blasted apart and then put together again.

408. In summer in Uranus, the Sun does not set for 20 years. In winter, darkness lasts for 20 years. In autumn, the sun rises and sets every 9 hours.

409. Einstein's theory of general relativity shows that gravity not only pulls on matter, but also space and even 'time' itself.

410. Earth's atmosphere was formed from gases pouring out from volcanoes.

411. Jupiter spins right round in less than 10 hours which means that the planet's surface is moving at nearly 50,000 km/hr.

412. True binary stars are two stars held together by one another's gravity, which spend their lives whirling around together like a pair of dancers.

413. Halley predicted that a comet he had discovered would return in 1758, 16 years after his death and it really did. It was the first time a comet's arrival had been predicted and the comet was named after him as Halley's Comet.

414. Ceres is the biggest asteroid in the Solar System - 940 km across and 0.0002% the size of the earth.

415. NASA's Voyager 2 spacecraft beamed back unprecedented data from interstellar space. It indicates a mysterious extra layer outside our solar system.

416. The Pioneer 10 and 11 probes carry metal plaques with messages for aliens telling them about us.

417. Astronauts learn scuba diving which helps them to deal with space walks.

418. The dog Laika, the first animal to go to space, died when the spacecraft's oxygen supply ran out.

419. The most distant galaxies (quasars) have red shifts so big that they must be moving away from us at speeds approaching the speed of light.

420. When light waves from distant galaxies are stretched out, they look redder. This is called Redshift.

421. The nuclear fusion reactions in the Sun's core send out billions of light photons every minute but they take 10 million years to reach its surface.

422. Einstein's theory of Special Relativity (1905) shows that all measurements are relative, including time and speed. In other words, time and speed depends upon where you measure them.

423. When things are falling, their acceleration cancels out gravity, which is why astronauts in orbits are weightless.

424. The Moon is the only other world that humans have set foot on.

425. Because the Moon has no atmosphere or wind, the footprints planted in its dusty surface in 1969 by the Apollo astronauts are still there today, perfectly preserved.

426. Richard Christopher Carrington found out about solar flares.

427. On the Moon's surface there are large dark patches called seas – because this is what people once believed they were. They are, in fact, lava flows from ancient volcanoes.

428. The brightest quasar is 3C 273, 2 billion light years away.

429. The brightest stars in the night sky are not actually stars, but the planets Jupiter, Venus, Mars and Mercury.

430. Jupiter's moon Europa may have oceans of water beneath its dry surface and it is a major target in the search for life in the Solar System.

431. Galaxies are often found in a group or clusters. One cluster may have 30 or so galaxies in it.

432. In the 1970's the US Vikings 1 and 2 and the Soviet Mars 3 and 5 probes all reached the surface of Mars.

433. The Milky Way belongs to a cluster of 30 galaxies called the Local Group, which is 7 million light years across.

434. The Virgo Cluster is 50 million light years away and is made up of 1000 galaxies.

435. For a satellite or a spacecraft to stay in orbit 200 km above the Earth, it has to fly over 8 km/sec.

436. When a spacecraft reaches 140% of the orbital velocity i.e. 11.2 km/sec, it is going fast enough to break free of the Earth's gravity. This is called escape velocity.

437. The Sun gets hot because it is so big that the pressure in its core is so tremendous - enough to force the nuclei of hydrogen atoms to fuse to make helium atoms. This nuclear reaction is like a gigantic atom bomb and it releases huge amounts of heat.

438. Dishes in the Space telescopes have to be made accurate two billionths of a millimetre.

439. You can see another galaxy with the naked eye: the Andromeda Galaxy, 2.2 million light years away.

440. Dried up riverbeds show that Mars probably once had water in its surface. There is sometimes ice at the poles and maybe water underground.

441. For a satellite to fly off into the space, its momentum should be greater than the pull of gravity of the Earth.

442. The future of the Universe may depend on how much dark matter there is. If there is too much, its gravity will eventually stop the Universe's expansion and make it shrink again.

443. According to astronauts, Space smells like seared steak, hot metal and welding fumes.

444. In 1962, the U.S. blew up a hydrogen bomb in Space that was 100 times more powerful than Hiroshima.

445. A sample of Isaac Newton's apple tree was sent to Space to prove and explain gravity.

446. In 1977, we received a signal from Deep Space that lasted 72 seconds. We still don't know how or where it came from.

447. The International Space Station is as roomy as a five-bedroom house and travels at 17,500 mph.

448. On the International Space Station, urine passes through a special water treatment plant that turns it into drinking water.

449. Space explorers from Russia are called 'cosmonauts.'

450. NASA is developing 3D printed pizzas for astronauts.

451. NASA scientists have discovered stars that are cool enough to touch.

452. Floating cities above the clouds of Venus may be our best bet for becoming a two-planet species. Conditions there are so similar to

Earth a human wouldn't need a pressurized suit, the gravity is similar and transit times are shorter than to Mars.

453. To our eyes, in Space, the Sun would appear white, not yellow.

454. Tortoises orbited the Moon before astronauts did; they were sent to test a Russian Space probe.

455. North Korea's Space agency is called NADA, which in Spanish means 'nothing.'

456. You can't whistle in Space.

457. Cockroaches that were raised in space were faster, stronger and tougher than cockroaches on Earth.

458. The farthest distance from Earth an astronaut has ever travelled was during the Apollo 13 emergency.

459. Astronauts on the International Space Station (ISS) exercise 2 hours per day.

460. The third country in Space, after The U.S. and the USSR, was Canada,

which was considered to have the most advanced space program in 1962.

461. *Apollo 13, Armageddon* and *Around the World in 80 Days* are among the movies NASA keeps aboard the International Space Station.

462. An astronaut threw a boomerang while visiting the International Space Station and it returned to him, even in the absence of gravity.

463. NASA has a list of accurate Space technology terms that writers can use in science fiction stories.

464. John F. Kennedy had such concerns about the Space program's high cost, that he proposed partnering with the Soviet Union on a joint expedition to the Moon.

465. Apollo 7 astronauts, Shirra, Eisele and Cunningham, made the first televised broadcast from Space in October 1968.

466. About 30% of solar radiation is reflected back to space and the rest is

absorbed by oceans, clouds and land masses.

467. The iron in our blood and the calcium in our bones came from ancient explosions of giant stars.

468. Outer Space is only an hour's drive away if you somehow drove your car straight upwards.

469. All astronauts must learn how to speak Russian and all cosmonauts must learn how to speak English.

470. El Godo is the largest galaxy cluster ever seen in the Universe.

471. The Universe is expanding at 74.3 km per second per megaparsec.

472. Astronauts don't snore in Space.

473. Ethiopia has a Space programme.

474. Sally Ride was the first American woman in Space.

475. In 2017, a group of scientists sent messages to any advanced alien civilization living in a star system

12.4 light years away, hoping to receive a response in 25 years.

476. During its lifetime, the International Space Station will be hit by 100,000 meteoroids.

477. According to a 1967 U.N. treaty, nobody can own celestial bodies such as Mars or the Moon.

478. The only survivors of the 2003 Columbia Space Shuttle disaster were some parasitic worms called nematodes.

479. The longest spacewalk ever lasted almost 9 hours.

480. The first words of the third man on the moon were, 'Whoopee! Man, that may have been a small one for Neil, but that's a long one for me.'

481. Night and day on Earth only appear to last 45 minutes from the International Space Station.

482. Comet Lovejoy released as much alcohol as the amount found in 500 bottles of wine every second during its peak activity.

483. Elementary school students in Virginia built a satellite that was later deployed into space by NASA in 2016.

484. Astronauts often lose their fingernails after conducting spacewalks.

485. In 1973, the crew of Skylab 4 staged the first strike in Space. They requested time off to 'look out of the window and think.'

486. It costs 41 cents per year per American citizen for NASA's entire Curiosity program.

487. While floating in lunar orbit, astronaut Al Worden was 2,235 miles (3,600 km) away from his companions, making him the most isolated human being ever.

488. The first animals in Space were fruit flies, launched in a rocket by the US in 1947. They were still living when it was recovered.

489. A meteor shower is lots of meteors from space.

490. There are 5 main dwarf planets.

491. There are 8 planets in the solar system.

492. The Kuiper belt was named after Gerard Kuiper.

493. The Oort cloud is named after Jan Oort.

494. The Perseids are sand to pea-sized bits of rocky debris that were ejected long ago by comet Swift-Tuttle.

495. What are Quadrantids? The Quadrantids, which peak during early-January each year, are considered to be one of the best annual meteor showers.

496. Aurigids is a meteor shower appearing in September.

497. Draconids is a meteor shower which appears in October.

498. The Alpha Monocerotids is a meteor shower active from 15 to 25 November every year.

499. The June Boötids is a meteor shower occurring roughly between 22 June and 2 July each year.

500. Webb's high-resolution infrared vision allows it to peer further into the Milky Way with greater clarity than infrared telescopes before it, uncovering parts of the galaxy that were once too dim, too distant, or too concealed to study.

A Final Message From Edwin.
There are lots of universes, lots of galaxies, lots of stars and lots of new things to be found in Space. There will be, one day, a planet waiting for us to go there. 'A time will come when men will stretch out their eyes. They should see planets like our Earth.' There will be stars and galaxies and universes waiting for us. There will be new scientists born, for my passion and chosen career is to be a scientist. This book is dedicated to all the human beings on Earth. Now that you know all about Space and the universe, please share this book with your family members and your friends. Thanks.